PAPER

PAPER

by

JEROME S. MEYER

Illustrated with photographs

THE WORLD PUBLISHING COMPANY

CLEVELAND AND NEW YORK

Published by The World Publishing Company
2231 West 110th Street, Cleveland 2, Ohio

Published simultaneously in Canada by
Nelson, Foster & Scott Ltd.

Library of Congress Catalog Card Number: 60-12899

FIRST EDITION

COWP

To my sister Mabel

PHOTO ACKNOWLEDGMENTS

The author and The World Publishing Company herewith thank the following institutions whose co-operation has made possible the preparation of *Paper*.

All possible care has been taken to trace the ownership of every picture included and to make full acknowledgment for its use. If any errors have accidentally occurred, they will be corrected in subsequent editions provided notification is sent to the publisher.

p. 60	American Forest Products Industries—Drix Duryea photo
p. 51, p. 54, p. 67	American Forest Products Industries—Gulf Oil Company photo
p. 27 (2)	Courtesy of the American Museum of Natural History
p. 41 (2), p. 47, p. 48, p. 64, p. 68, p. 70, p. 76, p. 77, p. 78 (top), p. 79 (2)	American Paper & Pulp Association
p. 45, p. 59, p. 65, p. 72	Courtesy of P. H. Glatfelter Company
pp. 14–15, p. 50, p. 57, p. 63, p. 69, p. 73, p. 78 (bot), p. 85	West Virginia Pulp and Paper Company

The author gratefully acknowledges the valuable help and advice given him by Mr. Theodore H. Davis, Director of Public Relations, American Paper and Pulp Association, and the executives of the P. H. Glatfelter Company of Spring Grove, Pennsylvania.

Without paper modern civilization
as we know it could not exist

1

Our daily lives are governed by inventions which we take as a matter of course. For example, most of us know nothing about the enormously complex dial telephone system with its vast labyrinth of conduits and hundreds of thousands of miles of hidden electric wires which enable us, in a matter of minutes, to converse with anyone anywhere in the civilized world. Huge jet planes are quickly becoming as commonplace as the telephone, for we no longer marvel at the possibility of leaving New York after an early breakfast and arriving in San Francisco at the beginning of the business day there the same day. TV programs which transport us thousands of miles around the world in a split second are also taken for granted, just as we accept casually the enormous bulk of the Sunday newspapers. It is part of modern living, and everything is taken for granted without giving the inventors, engineers, and financial promoters a second's thought.

But it's not only modern inventions that we take for granted. We shop at large department stores and super- markets where there are hundreds of thousands of dif- ferent items on counters and shelves for us to choose from. Most of them are neatly wrapped and packaged and boxed, all ready and waiting for us to buy them and take them away. How they were made and packaged and how, by our extremely complicated and highly effi- cient system of merchandising and distribution, they got into the large and small stores all over the country most of us know little and care less.

One of the greatest inventions, and one of the most important in our world today, is one we see and use every day of our lives without thinking twice about it. That invention is paper.

Imagine what your life would be like today if there were no paper. Just suppose that all the paper in the world vanished overnight and you awoke to learn that there was no such thing as paper of any kind anywhere. At first, you probably would not realize the disastrous consequences or what would happen to this strange and different world you were in. You would get up and wash and dress as usual and sit down to breakfast. If you were accustomed to having dry cereal, you would have to do without it, because all packaged products in containers or cardboard boxes would have vanished. It is quite possible that you would have no breakfast at all, at least at the beginning, since it would be difficult to buy bread, butter, eggs, and even milk, all of which are now either wrapped in paper or put up in paperboard containers.

As you looked around your room you would find that all the pictures on the wall had vanished as well as all the books in the bookcases and the magazines in the magazine rack. No sign of paper anywhere and, of course, your notebooks and homework would have vanished too.

While you were trying to get used to this peculiar situation you would probably begin to hear noise and confusion in the street, and when you looked out the window, you would see milling crowds, worried and angry, going nowhere because there would be nowhere to go. All business houses, from the largest corporation to the tiniest store, would have to close, because they are dependent on paper for bills, files, and bookkeeping and accounting records. There are no ready substitutes for paper for this use. Business everywhere would be at a complete standstill, and everyone would be out of work.

You might have an impulse to go to the door and pick up the morning newspaper to read what's going on, but of course, there would be no paper there. And if you turned on the radio or TV to get the news, no sounds would come from them, because most loudspeaker cones are paper. They would have vanished too.

Of course, there could be no mail of any description . . . no letters or post cards or circulars or advertising matter or any other kind of mail, not to mention the lack of postage stamps. Without paper, every post office, mail-order house, and advertising agency would have to close. The same would be true for every bank, since all banks are entirely dependent upon paper: paper money, checks, notes, bonds, stocks, drafts, and scores of other important documents. Try to imagine business today without paper money or checks or stock certificates, and you'll see how impossible it would be.

Scores of giant industries whose products seemingly have nothing whatever to do with paper would have to close too. The drug and bottling and canning industries, for example, might seem to have no connection with paper. Surely glass bottles and metal cans are far removed from it. But imagine the utter confusion if all the jars and bottles and cans in our drugstores and groceries had no labels to identify them.

Most of the paper mentioned above is used for writing or printing; and, indeed, 50 per cent of all paper manufactured is used for this purpose. But millions of tons of paper are manufactured for uses that have no connection with printing or writing. Wrapping paper and paper bags, paper napkins and plates and cups, towels, cleansing tissues, toilet paper, waxed papers, and thousands of other specialty papers are a few examples.

Also in this same category are filter papers, building paper, cigarette paper, all kinds of paperboard boxes and cartons of every size and description. In the United States alone in one year paperboard, sometimes called *cardboard,* is produced in a quantity great enough to cover the area taken up by the states of Vermont, New Hampshire, and Delaware. Just look into the window of any drugstore or stationer in your city or town and count the number of items either made of paper or wrapped in it. The same applies to any supermarket. The logs from which all paper is made in the United States in one year, placed end to end, would stretch for more than 2 million miles, or almost ten times the distance from here to the moon!

Paper is civilization itself, and its invention ranks in importance with the taming of fire and the invention of the wheel. Without it, every newspaper, magazine, and book publisher; every business house and every store; every law court, college, school, and library would be forced to close, and the entire industrial and social life of America would be at a complete standstill.

Perhaps this seems a great exaggeration. Surely iron and steel and aluminum are much more important, especially when we think of the millions of different machines in our factories: the thousands of printing presses

A typical American family of four uses approximately 1,700 pounds of paper a year

and linotype machines and looms and trains and auto-
mobiles and airplanes and everything else made of steel
and iron and aluminum. These and countless other
articles that we see and use daily are made of metal,
and paper doesn't enter into them at all. Why, then, is
paper civilization itself?

The answer is simple: *Paper records all knowledge.* No
idea, no invention, no new project, could be developed
and produced without first planning it on paper. All the
wonderful things we see around us, from the simplest
machine to the tallest skyscraper or largest jet plane,
must first pass through the planning stage before it can
be made, and it is impossible to conceive how plans for
anything can be drawn without the use of paper.

The amount of paper used for planning the average
skyscraper—the blueprints, specifications, etc.—runs well
over a ton, and it has been estimated that the construction of a large aircraft carrier requires nearly a hundred
tons of paper, including a whole carload of blueprints.

There are scores of different kinds of papers. Book and
magazine paper comes in various grades and weights
and finishes. The amount of such paper used is stagger-
ing. In the United States, there are more than 50 million
books and over a billion magazines, each averaging
about one hundred pages, printed in one year. All this
book and magazine paper, if cut into sheets the size of

this page, would cover the State of Connecticut with plenty of paper left over. Then there is newsprint paper which, as the name implies, is used for newspapers and is not so white and smooth as book and magazine paper. A single copy of the Sunday edition of *The New York Times* contains more than 600 pages, with a circulation of well over a million copies. This means that in only one day more than 600 million large sheets of newsprint paper are used and distributed by only one of the hundreds of newspapers in this country. There is blotting paper and tissue paper and wrapping paper. And there are many, many more kinds, some very thin and others very thick, in the form of cardboard or paperboard. All kinds of paper contribute to and build the vast industries which provide us with the comforts of modern living.

2

Long before the dawn of civilization men were able to communicate with one another vocally. What languages they used are unknown, of course, but men were able to make their thoughts understood by various sounds. This was the most primitive method of communication, for even animals can convey certain impressions to one another through sound. It was only when primitive man learned to record his thoughts that he raised himself to a new intellectual level. Here was a way to put down a thought and keep it there for others to see. The first recordings, as we all know, were in the form of childlike drawings which later developed into *hieroglyphics,* stylized pictures or symbols representing words, sounds, or ideas. The impressions were carved in stone, first on the walls of caves and later on stone slabs. The Rosetta stone in the British Museum at London and the obelisk—known as Cleopatra's Needle—in Central Park in New York City are excellent examples of this primitive writing as it developed in ancient Egypt.

Today it is difficult for us to realize what an important step learning to write was. Thoughts, instead of vanishing into air on sound waves, could "stay put" forever and be conveyed to others, to one's children, grandchildren, great-grandchildren. As more and more of the ancient peoples learned to record their thoughts the art of writing was born. Because stone was a difficult, heavy, and cumbersome medium, man looked around for other more practical substitutes. The early Romans used leaves of trees on which to inscribe their messages, but these were not too practical because the writing had to be extremely delicate.

As early as the second century B.C. men began using the split skin of sheep and other animals, known as *parchment*. This excellent writing medium was first produced in the ancient city of Pergamum (now Bergama) in Asia Minor and was so ideally suited to the needs of the ancients that it was used right up until the time of the invention of paper. We still give this name to a fine paper having the texture of parchment.

A writing surface that was widely used by the ancient Egyptians was made from the papyrus plant. The pith from the papyrus stalk was extracted and cut into thin strips, placed side by side and forming the base for a second set of strips which was pasted crosswise over the first to form a sheet. The paste was made of wheat flour and muddy water from the Nile, sometimes mixed with vinegar. The sheet was then dried in the sun and beaten smooth with mallets. On the finished papyrus the ancient Egyptians wrote with the ancestors of our pen and ink: a thick, sharp stick dipped in the juice of berries.

As writing developed and civilizations became more complex a new and better medium for writing was necessary. It was the Chinese who invented it.

For centuries ancient Chinese scholars had been putting down their thoughts in books printed with wood blocks on thin rice paper, and writing on such materials as bone, bronze, and silk. They especially worked with strips of bamboo, using a pointed stylus as a marking instrument. While bamboo was the standard medium of China for years, it was never particularly satisfactory, since the writing surface cracked and was difficult to read and preserve. It was not until the third century B.C. that the stylus gave way to the brush, a regular pointed paintbrush which, when dipped in the juice of berries, produced much better writing. It did not take the Chinese intellectuals long to realize that this brush worked better on cloth than a stylus on bamboo. Cloth became the new medium on which to write, and it was through the examination of cloth that the importance of fibers was discovered.

Fibers are the essence of paper and cloth. You cannot

have paper in the true sense unless it is made up of infinitesimal fibers matted together. It was understanding this principle that led the way to the invention of paper in the year 105 A.D.

The inventor was a Chinese scholar who was an official in the court of the Emperor Ho Ti. The scholar's name was Tsai Lun. His invention was undoubtedly one of the most important in history, but it took men another 1,700 years to learn to produce paper as we know it today in quantity.

In those early days the cloth used for writing was scarce, so Tsai Lun began to experiment with mulberry bark, hemp, and water. He did this by mashing sodden bark and hemp into a pulp and pressing out the liquid. The pulp that remained was then hung up on boards to dry in the sun, and the uneven, rough sheet that resulted was the first paper. Tsai Lun's method of papermaking was crude, yet effective. We don't know too much about the construction of his papermaking "machine," but it is safe to say that it was merely a large square of very coarsely woven cloth held tightly in a bamboo frame. The frame was dipped vertically into water containing ground-up, softened mulberry bark fibers and was then tilted under the floating fibers. When the frame was lifted out, the fibers stuck to it and the water drained through the cloth. The softened fibers were then heated and dried in the sun to form a smooth whitish-gray surface.

The mulberry bark Tsai Lun used was mashed up and pulverized by hammering it in a stone trough, known as a *mortar,* before it was floated in water. As a matter of fact, there is still preserved today in the Imperial Museum in Honan, China, the very mortar Tsai Lun used some 1,800 years ago. At that time he could not possibly have realized that his discovery that the wood fibers in mulberry bark made adequate paper would someday be of utmost importance to the world. He only knew that this new medium was just as good and perhaps better than either bamboo or cloth, although cloth in the form of hemp did enter into his paper process. What he actually discovered and produced for his own time was paper made on the basic principle of meshing fibers on a screen with plenty of water to unite them. And that is the same principle used in papermaking today.

To compare Tsai Lun's first paper with the paper we have today is like comparing a little footbridge over a country stream with the Golden Gate Bridge in San Francisco. Only the principle is the same, but it is the basic principle. Nearly two thousand years ago few people could read and write, and there was little need or reason for mass production of printed materials even if such a thing had been possible in those days. The few books there were, were printed from wood blocks; movable type was not invented until 1,300 years later. Under these circumstances it is obvious that the value of Tsai Lun's discovery and invention was little appreciated, nor was it used to any great extent except by the scholars and favored few who were able to afford books or manuscripts.

The new method of producing paper became well known in the Orient within a short time, however. Many books, such as they were, were made for those who could read and who could afford them. By the seventh century papermaking had spread to Japan and Korea, and the Japanese added further knowledge to the art. Japan was and still is famous for its paper, and the craftsmen of Japan have long been masters in developing various kinds of paper, all based on the elementary principle of using the fibers of plants combined with water and rags for a screen. Paper was produced in fairly large quantities in both China and Japan, but it was all done by hand on screens. None of it was produced by machinery the way it is today.

Naturally, when we think of paper in connection with Japan, we immediately think of rice paper. This is not paper at all. Even though it is a beautiful medium for Japanese and Chinese prints and paintings, it is not manufactured or made the way paper is made. Rice paper is made from the pith of a certain plant which grows in the hills of northern Formosa.

It took quite a while for papermaking to spread westward into Europe. We don't know exactly when it was first introduced into Spain and Italy, but we do know that it took more than a thousand years after its invention in China for European civilization to realize the importance of paper. Italy was probably the first European country to produce paper in any quantity. Beautiful books, hand-illuminated in color and printed from wood blocks, were produced in Italy and Germany before the great revolution in printing took place.

This began about 1438 when Johann Gutenberg, a specialized printer in the little town of Mainz, Germany, succeeded in making movable type in metal molds. This meant that for the first time books could be printed quickly and cheaply, and immediately the need for paper assumed worldwide importance. Movable type ranks in importance with the greatest of inventions, because it forms the basis of all printing everywhere. Without it there could be no inexpensive books, no newspapers, and no printed matter, and thus, no spreading of knowledge.

The first book to be printed from movable type was a Latin Bible, now usually called the *Gutenberg Bible*. It is believed to have been published in 1456. The paper was made from cloth, each sheet being dipped into a solution of gelatin which acted as a sort of glue and stiffener. The cloth rags formed a hard surface. As time went on and more books were produced, cotton rags were in great demand and were manufactured especially for the production of paper. It is most interesting to note that Tsai Lun's method of making paper with other plant fibers (mulberry bark and hemp) was apparently overlooked. For many, many years, paper was manufactured in Europe exclusively from old rags.

By the middle of the seventeenth century, books and even newspapers were fairly prevalent and the mills that were making cotton for the production of paper had to work at top speed to supply the demand.

Not long after this, René Antoine Ferchault de Reaumur, a well-known French naturalist and physicist, began studying the habits of insects. He became interested in wasps, and after examining their nests and carefully analyzing them, he found that they were made of a sort of paper and nothing more. This was an amazing discovery.

This insect is really a professional papermaker. It chews up wood and plant fibers into a powder which it mixes with an adhesive produced in its own body. This results in a fine pulp which the insect eventually transforms into many layers of paper in a remarkable manner.

25

The paper is exceptionally light, dark gray in color, and quite tough. It is also water resistant. Reaumur found that it was as good in quality as most light paper being made in France at that time.

Reaumur then studied the habits of the American wasp and observed that the insect actually produced paper from wood fibers taken from old fences or shingles. He made a great many notes and careful observations and finally read his findings before the French Royal Academy on November 15, 1719. This is what he said: "The American wasps form very fine paper, like ours; they extract the fibres of common wood of the countries where they live. They teach us that paper can be made from the fibres of plants without the use of rags and linen, and seem to invite us to try whether we cannot make fine and good paper from the use of certain woods. If we had woods similar to those used by the American wasps for their paper, we could make the whitest paper, for this material is very white. By a further beating and breaking of the fibres that the wasps make and using the thin paste that comes from them, a very fine paper may be composed. This study should not be neglected, for it is, I dare say, important. The rags from which we make our paper are not an economical material and every papermaker knows that this substance is becoming rare. While the consumption of paper in-

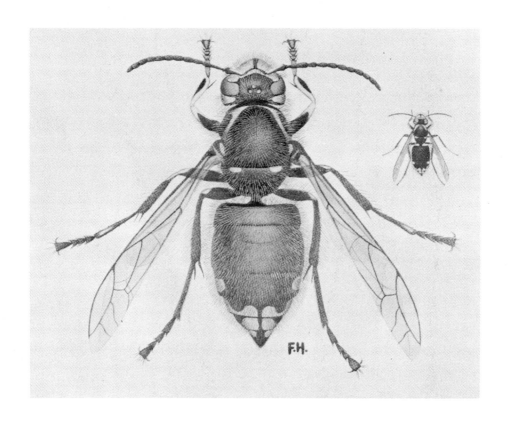

A wasp, the very first papermaker, uses its product to build its nest

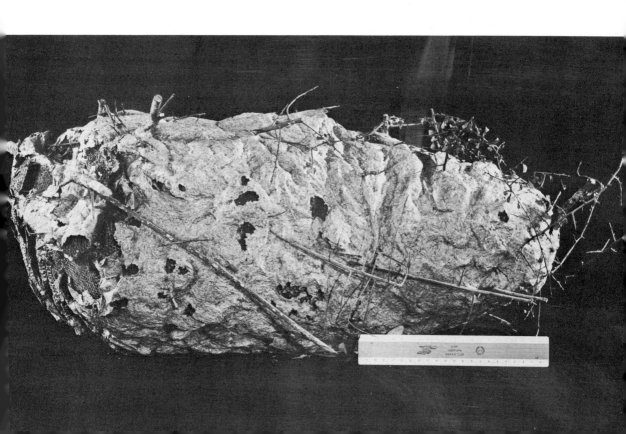

creases every day, the production of linen remains about the same. In addition to this the foreign mills draw upon us for material. The wasp seems to teach us a means of overcoming these difficulties."

Reaumur continued his observations regarding a heavier wasp-made paper: "But all of the wasps that I know make nothing as singular as a species of wasp that lives in Canada . . . At first glance, and even after examining the surface for a considerable time, one would accept the nest as the work of the hand of man. Its covering resembles our paper to such an extent that it is hard to detect a difference. It has the same gloss, and the colour is that of an old piece of manufactured paper which had formerly been white."

Reaumur's speech before the French Royal Academy had no effect upon the papermakers of Europe. Here was the lesson of the wasp, the very first papermaker, brought out and given in clear unmistakable terms; yet nobody gave a thought to the wood from trees as an important substitute for rags. Of course, the speech was applauded and published, but that is all that came of it and for more than a century after Reaumur, manufacturers continued producing paper from old rags and fibrous plants in a slow, tedious, single-sheet hand process not too different from the early methods of ancient China.

This is not surprising. New revolutionary ideas are always slow to take root. People are either skeptical or too busy to bother. A fine example of an important discovery in a different field from paper was given by Thomas Edison shortly after he invented the electric light. Edison experimented with the glowing filament and noticed that a current flowed from the filament to a copper plate which he had inserted inside the bulb. He thought it interesting and gave a talk on it, calling it the "Edison Effect." It made no impression on the scientists of the day and lay dormant for more than fifty years. It was not until Sir John Fleming and Lee De Forest investigated the Edison Effect further that the first vacuum tube was made, and radio and television were born.

When we think of paper, we naturally think of printing and writing. Printing and writing are to paper as butter is to bread. More than half the paper made today is printed or written upon, so it is no wonder that the demand for paper increased enormously as new and better printing methods were invented.

Because of the effect of printing on the production of paper it is important to dwell briefly here on the history of the printing press after Gutenberg produced the first book from movable type.

The printing press has come a long way since the days when Johann Gutenberg used his first movable type. The press of his day was a crude wooden affair, consist-

ing of two upright posts held together by heavy crosspieces, top and bottom. There were also two other big
wooden crosspieces, one to hold the flat "bed" upon
which the type was placed, the other, a flat wooden
"platen" attached to a large wooden screw. The type
was inked with a ball made of leather and stuffed with
wool, and the ink was usually some concoction of dark
dye. The operator spread paper over the inked type, lay-
ing a piece of blanket or some other soft material on it
to keep the paper from tearing. Then the large screw
was turned by hand until the pressure of the platen on
the paper was enough to transfer the type impression.
This took a great deal of time, sometimes as long as
three minutes per impression. Just imagine printing a
full issue of a national magazine at the rate of three
minutes a page: it would take about five thousand years
to produce a single edition!

It took nearly four hundred years for the printing
press to evolve into what we might consider a fairly
modern machine. After many years, the old screw hand
press gave way to the lever principle of making impressions, and while the lever principle was being explored
and improved upon, many experiments were made on
an entirely new and revolutionary design. Among the
very first to make such experiments was a brilliant German engineer, Friedrich König, who visited England in

1806 and spent five years trying to harness power to a platen-type machine which he had invented.

It occurred to König that a steam-motor-driven revolving cylinder, pressing sheet after sheet against flat type on a flat bed, could turn out printed pages much faster than the old vertical lever press. So in 1810 he made the first cylinder press. In this radically different printing press, the form in which the prepared type was locked, was placed on a flat bed with a cylinder directly above it. This cylinder had a threefold motion. The first third of the turn received the sheet upon one of the cylinders and secured it there; the second third rolled along to take the impression of the type. The printed sheet was then removed by hand, and the last motion of the cylinder returned the tympan, empty, to its original position to receive another sheet.

This was the first rotary press, the forerunner of the modern printing press. Two years after he made this new machine, König patented an important improvement. The part of the periphery of the cylinder not used for taking the impression of the type was slightly reduced in diameter, so as to allow the form to return under it freely after the impression. This new press also carried a movable type bed geared to the sides of the machine and free to slide back and forth in a reciprocating motion. All high-speed presses throughout the world today are rotary presses. Nearly every newspaper, magazine, and book is printed on highly improved cylinder rotary presses, based on the principle discovered and patented by König.

König's first press printed the London *Times,* turning it out at the rate of 1,100 sheets per hour. Many improvements for printing and handling the sheets were subsequently made, and double-cylinder presses were soon able to print four thousand sheets per hour.

It is difficult to understand how, in spite of the thousands of books, magazines, and newspapers that were being printed in Europe and America in the late 18th century, all paper was still made entirely by hand from rags and fibrous plants. The paper turned out, while fairly good, was never enough. Such rapid strides in the art of printing, such new and radical improvements in printing presses caused a demand for paper never known before and one which far outweighed the supply. If a single press could print four thousand sheets an hour, and presses just as fast and faster were being built everywhere, the primitive method of paper production had to be improved and stepped up.

And then the inevitable happened! The very first paper machine was invented in 1798 by Nicolas Louis Robert, a native of Paris.

Robert, a young man with unusual mechanical ability,

held a responsible position in the long-established paper mill of François Didot in Essonnes, France. One of Robert's main duties was to supervise the personnel and see that everything was going smoothly. Paper was still made entirely by hand in a very slow and laborious manner and the employees had to work long hours for little pay. This naturally created a great deal of discontent and dissension, and it was while Robert was trying to ease this seemingly hopeless situation that his mind turned to the idea of a papermaking machine.

The more Robert thought of it, the more enthusiastic he became. There was no question in his mind that machinery was the only solution to the ever-increasing paper problem. He worked hard and long, sketching out different designs, and when he finally submitted the one he thought would actually work, Didot was greatly impressed. They worked together to make a working model from Robert's design, but unfortunately when it was finished, it was too cumbersome and impractical to do what it was supposed to do. In the face of this discouragement, Robert made many new models at great expense, and finally succeeded in producing the world's first workable papermaking machine.

The basic operation of Robert's machine was the same as that used in papermaking machines today: to dissolve fibers in running water over closely woven moving

33

screens, allowing the water to drain through and leaving the fibers on the moving screens. The flat sheets of wet fibers were removed and hung up to dry just as had been done for centuries before with handmade paper. The idea of passing the wet paper over heated cylinders or absorbing the wetness with felt, as is done today, never occurred to Robert.

Robert is credited with the invention of modern paper, but there are other names just as important as his in its development. True, it was Robert who made the first papermaking machine. He was also the first to produce a continuous sheet in a size greater than any paper previously made. This was certainly a definite advance in the art of papermaking. Robert's machine was able to turn out larger and better sheets much faster and more economically than any handmade paper anywhere at that time.

In 1801, the Fourdrinier brothers, who were London stationers, became interested in Robert's model. They saw that this invention offered the possibility of catching up with the ever-increasing demand for paper, but they also noted many drawbacks in the original machine. They produced and perfected the first practical moving screen, and got some of the finest engineers of the day to work on the improvement and development of paper-making machinery. Through their efforts a great many

34

new and important improvements were made. Modern papermaking machines using a flat-bed wire screen are still called *Fourdrinier machines.* However, an error in the wording of the brothers' patents enabled others to use the improvements they made, and in a few years hundreds of papermaking machines appeared all over Europe.

Up to this time, the magic key that was to unlock the secret of paper production in huge quantities was still missing. The machinery was good but not good enough, so it remained for John Dickinson of Hertfordshire, England, to create and perfect the first rotary papermaking machine in 1809.

Dickinson immersed a huge cylinder covered with a woven wire screen into a vat of liquid pulp and rotated it in such a way that the pulp adhered to the screen and formed very wet paper. The paper was then detached and passed onto another large cylinder covered with felt which dried it. The dried paper was then heated and passed through other rollers, coming out in a continuous unlimited length as fine, clean, strong paper.

The name of John Dickinson stands out prominently as one of the leading pioneers in the art of quantity paper production. His machine was such a great improvement on those that had gone before that the entire paper-making industry boomed. Now it was possible to produce rolls and rolls of paper quickly and easily and thus supply the ever-increasing demand. But there was still one big drawback to the paper situation. The new machinery speeded production, but paper was still made from cloth, and in spite of the many brilliant scientists who were working on the problem, no one had found a substitute for the ever-dwindling supply of rags. The lesson of the wasp was still ignored, and Reaumur's name had passed into history.

England must have full credit for the invention of improved paper machinery, but the final link in the chain of events that led to the paper we now have in our homes was forged in Germany. In 1840, one hundred twenty-one years after Reaumur's speech about the wasp paper-makers, Friedrich Gottlob Keller, a German weaver in Hainichen, Saxony, secured a patent for a wood-grinding machine. The germ of the idea for this machine came to him while watching children grind the convex sides from cherry pits to make beads by holding them against a wet grindstone with a notched block of wood. In so doing, part of the wooden block was defibered by friction against the stone. Keller squeezed some of these damp wood-fibers in his hand and noticed that they felted together. This simple observation was the beginning of Keller's wood-grinding machine. With the financial help of Heinrich Voelter, a paper-mill director, Keller launched a new era in papermaking.

The machine was destined to undergo a wonderful development and give to the world inexpensive ground-wood paper, mainly newsprint paper. Because of its low cost, it made possible the modern newspaper with its unlimited dissemination of the news. At last, paper could be made exclusively from wood. From 1840 on, paper mills all over the world started substituting wood fibers from trees—pine, poplar, spruce, oak, and others—for the fibers of old rags and plants which had been used since the time of Tsai Lun.

But paper for printing and dissemination of knowledge was only half the story. Another vitally important demand for paper came from the large and small businesses and manufacturing firms all over Europe. As more things were manufactured and stocks of goods increased, it became necessary to find some means of wrapping or packaging the various items. Cardboard boxes, cartons, and wrapping paper began to take the place of wooden boxes and baskets. Manufacturers and retailers found that cardboard boxes and cartons were much lighter, more practical, and less expensive for shipping purposes than wooden crates and boxes. In view of this greatly increased demand for paper, something had to be done to increase the supply—some radically new method of production and, far more important, some new source of supply other than rags and fibrous plants.

The papermaking machine of today is extremely complicated and would require a small book in itself to explain the intricate workings of its many parts. Most of the machines contain as many as one hundred cylinders acting as slowly rotating boilers which heat and dry the paper as it is interwoven among them. The modern machine is longer than a football field, turning out as much as three and a half miles of paper every fifteen minutes.

3

All paper, whether modern or ancient, comes from growing plants. When paper was made from rags, the rags in turn had been made from cotton, also originally a plant. Other sources of paper in the past have been pulp or fiber from straw, flax, hemp, bamboo, and similar growing plants. It is only within the last hundred years that trees from the forest have yielded the millions of tons of paper used annually in the United States.

Paper today is made from wood fibers, water, and chemicals. That is very important to remember! *Wood fibers and water and chemicals make more than 90 per cent of all the paper you see and use.* It is impossible to make paper in the vast quantities and varieties used today without wood. It is equally impossible to make paper without water. It takes, on the average, 175 gallons of water to produce one pound of paper. Without water all paper mills would be out of business. That is why they are referred to as *mills* instead of *factories.* Most people know that paper is made from wood, but few realize the importance of water.

Wood is really billions of tiny fibers no more than $\frac{1}{32}$ inch long and as fine as a spider web, all bound together in a solid chunk by lignin (a sticky organic substance much like glue). When the lignin and sap and resin in wood are removed by chemical means, the loose fibers, floating in suspension in water, become wood pulp.

In modern papermaking, the wood pulp—which is 99 per cent water—is sent into the huge machines where the water containing the billions of tiny fibers, flows like a brook over a moving screen of fine wire. This screen, turning continuously on rollers, moves along rapidly under the flowing water, which quickly seeps through the screen, depositing wet fibers on it. The fibers cling to one another and mat together to form a large sheet-like mass. As the screen moves along, it carries this water-soaked mass to huge rollers where, with the aid of felt, it is dried and passed over large rotating cylinders which further dry it and press it somewhat the way your mother might use a hot iron to iron out a handkerchief. That, very briefly, is the basis of modern papermaking.

We have already mentioned some of the many different kinds of paper we see and use every day. Some, like toilet tissue or kleenex, are very loosely woven and fragile; others, like notebook and ledger paper and the

Papermaking today begins with trees

paper in this or any other book, are tight and tough. These great differences among papers are the result of many specific operations performed in the course of making the paper, but most of the differences are due mainly to the following: (1) the kind of wood pulp originally used; (2) the speed of the papermaking machine; (3) the nature of the materials added to the pulp, such as resin, starch, alum, and glue; (4) the finishing treatment given the paper after leaving the machine.

Before we explain these various processes, try this simple experiment: Take a sheet of cleansing or toilet tissue and hold it to the light. Notice how thin it is and how the light penetrates it. The fibers are very loosely woven as you can see if you examine the tissue with a magnifying glass. If you try to write on it with ink, the ink will be absorbed by the fibers and run in all directions. Now try to pull the tissue apart (not tear it), and you will see that it comes apart as easily as a ball of cotton. It is just as easy to pull it apart as it is to tear it apart. And when you do this, you can see the tiny fibers clearly. Of course, if you wet this tissue, it will become a soft pulpy mass, no longer paper.

Having seen for yourself how "un-paperlike" this tissue really is, throw it in a pot of water and stir it thoroughly. It will gradually disintegrate and become a spongy mass in the water. This is because the fibers are loosely matted and are almost pure bleached wood pulp without many other materials added.

In paper toweling, on the other hand, the fibers are closer together and sizing has been added to give the paper more body. It will absorb water but will not disintegrate when thrown into water.

Now, tear a sheet of paper out of your notebook or from a writing pad. Look closely at this sheet. It is usually white and opaque. If you hold it to the light, you won't be able to see the fibers clearly. This opacity is due to several reasons. For one thing, the forward action of the machine in which the paper was made was set to a slow speed which allowed the fibers to mesh more tightly together on the moving screen. Secondly, certain things were added to the pulp to strengthen it. That is why the paper is opaque when held to light. If you try to pull the note paper apart the way you did the tissue, you will find it is quite impossible. You can tear it, but you cannot pull it apart.

Obviously this paper is much tougher and quite different from tissue. If you put your pen to it, the ink will not spread through the fibers. If you put such paper in water, it will not easily disintegrate. It is hard and crackly, in contrast to the softness and wooliness of the tissue.

Most people are unaware that the kind of paper

which a mill turns out is formulated in advance just the way chemists formulate a new type of drug. Each kind must have a certain brightness, strength, finish, bulk, opacity, and cleanliness. The requirements of a specific type of paper must also take into consideration its receptivity to ink, its printing surface, permanence, and other physical properties such as smoothness, density, stiffness, and resistance to folding and tearing. In special cases, paper must undergo unusually severe tests in folding. United States paper currency is a good example of this; obviously if our money began to break up after ten or fifteen foldings, it would indeed be useless.

The rate of flow of the water into the papermaking machine and the speed of the machine itself are also carefully figured out for each specific kind of paper.

We have already emphasized the importance of water. Water enters into every step of papermaking, from the making of the pulp to the making of the finished paper. Naturally, all impurities must be removed so that the water is as good as the finest drinking water. For this reason water used from lakes and rivers is filtered several times and retained in a reservoir until it is used. If this were not done, the page which you are reading would have many little specks in it which would interfere with the printing on it.

What is true of the purity of water is just as true for

Water enters into every step of papermaking

the purity of the pulp. The process of transforming wooden logs into the finest, purest, and whitest pulp is the story of modern paper.

Paper production today may be divided into two main classifications: the *chemical process* and the *groundwood, or mechanical, process*. The chemical process produces the best paper from the standpoint of surface, durability, and smoothness. There are many different methods of making paper by the chemical process. The one described here is called the *soda process*.

THE CHEMICAL PROCESS

In forests far and near, woodsmen are constantly chopping down trees eight or more inches in diameter and sawing them into logs about five feet long. Depending upon their location, these logs are either floated downriver or sent by rail or truck to the mills, where they are stored in large piles until needed.

When this time comes, the logs are dumped into a conveyor where they are fed into a huge, slowly rotating, iron drum. Here they are subjected to heavy streams of water which clean and prepare the bark for separation from the wood and are then tossed and tumbled and bumped and jammed against one another until

46

Logs are stored in the mill's woodyard until they are ready for use

The bark is removed from logs by water pressure and friction

all their bark has been knocked off by constant friction.

The debarked logs are then led by another conveyor to the chipping room where the large powerful knives of the chipping machine, rotating at great speed, reduce them to small chips of wood the size of a book of matches. These small chips—millions of them—are passed over screens where all remaining particles of bark are removed. They are then stored in tanks, each tank holding chips of different tree species.

When the make-up of the kind of paper desired is formulated and the type of wood specified, chips from that particular storage tank are fed into the digesters for the "cooking" process.

The digesters are enormous cast-iron tanks more than three stories high and thirty feet in diameter. They operate just like giant pressure cookers. The chips needed to make the required quantity of pulp are dumped into them, sodium hydroxide is added, and the tops of the digesters are bolted tight. As soon as the bolts are secure, hot steam, at the enormous pressure of 125 pounds per square inch, is admitted and the chips start to "cook." In this cooking process which continues for hours, the cellulose fibers are separated from lignin, resin, and sap. What remains is a steaming, hot, black, pulpy, molten mass somewhat like hot tar. This is the beginning of the

Pulpwood chips are carried to the digester by conveyor belt

Digesters, more than three stories high, operate like enormous pressure cookers

papermaking process which will eventually transform this black, ugly, smelly mass into smooth, clean, white paper just like the page you are now reading.

Chemistry is extremely important in the process of papermaking. We just mentioned sodium hydroxide as one of the ingredients which was put into the digester. This is a salt known as *caustic soda,* or *lye.* It is really more than a salt. It is a very powerful alkali (a water-soluble substance that can neutralize acids) and, like all alkalis, it acts to remove impurities and foreign substances from, in this case, wood. Pure sodium hydroxide is extremely active and is dangerous to use. Very small amounts of it, however, together with a great deal of animal fat and perfume, is used in soaps. It is the extremely small percentage of caustic soda in soap that removes dirt and foreign matter from your hands and face and cleans you. Of course, lye and caustic soda in more concentrated forms are used as cleansers around the house, but they are always labeled dangerous and poisonous. So concentrated sodium hydroxide will attack foreign matter and set it free. Under extreme heat and pressure it is even more active and that is why, with other chemicals, it releases the millions of tiny fibers in the wood from the sap and lignin and resin and sets them free.

The next step in the transformation of wood to white

pulp takes place when the black tarlike pulp is fed into large cylindrical drums which rotate slowly, washing it constantly until all traces of chemicals and bits of resin are removed. As the drums slowly rotate, water gushes from little pipes to soak and wash the black pulp completely. After passing through two or three of these large drums, the pulp gradually takes on a brownish color, the color of wrapping paper. It is now almost pure unbleached pulp floating on a rapid stream of water which leads it to the bleaching room where it goes through three separate stages.

The first stage is known as *chlorination*. Here the pulp enters more huge drums where it is mixed with quantities of chlorine dioxide gas, which is a bleaching agent.

The chemistry of this is simple. The molecules of a gas normally contain two atoms. That is why hydrogen is written H_2, oxygen is written O_2, chlorine is written Cl_2, and hardly ever H, O, and Cl.

Under certain conditions oxygen and chlorine molecules sometimes contain only one atom. When this happens, the very strong single atom grabs onto any matter that's available in order to return the molecule to its natural balance. That is why hydrogen peroxide (H_2O_2), which is nothing more than water (H_2O) and an extra atom of oxygen, is used as a disinfectant. The extra atom seizes on any foreign matter in a small wound and re-

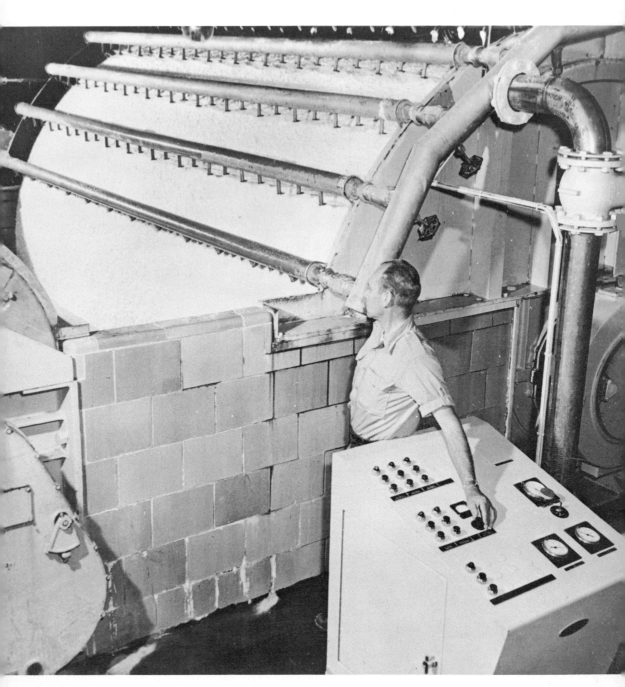

*The pulp is thoroughly washed in a series of large cylindrical drums
to remove all traces of chemicals and bits of resin*

moves the poison. Hydrogen peroxide also removes dye, particularly from hair, which explains the expression "peroxide blonde." It means that dark hair can be lightened by hydrogen peroxide due to the fact that some of the dark brown color of the hair is washed out along with the extra single atom of oxygen.

You can see that this one-atom molecule of oxygen, called *nascent oxygen,* is very active. In the chlorine bleaching process used on pulp this nascent oxygen appears again and is even more active.

The combination of water and gas produces a chemical reaction in which the nascent oxygen grabs hold of the brown material in the pulp and is washed away with it, leaving the pulp a yellowish-tan color. Again it is washed and thoroughly cleaned before it is led into a second rotating drum where it is further bleached and purified. The second drum rotates very slowly, thoroughly washing out all the impurities and coloring matter that might be left over from the first drum. The pulp is then led into the third drum for a final washing and soaking. This time weak sulfuric acid is mixed with it to eliminate all traces of the original caustic soda, chlorine, and other impurities. When it leaves the third drum, the pulp is pure white, a fluffy mass resembling white popcorn as it floats along on water-filled troughs. You might have an urge to pick it up, thinking it is popcorn, but if you did, you would find that its fluffiness and bulk is about 95 per cent water and only 5 per cent pure pulp. The whiteness of the pulp is determined by the degree of chlorination, its purity by the degree of washing and screening. The conveyor leads the pulp into huge tanks similar in size to the digester tanks, and there it remains until it is needed.

Before the pulp can enter the tremendous papermaking machine to be turned into the smooth, clean paper that you see on this page, the wood fibers themselves have to be processed. If something were not done to them—if they were allowed to float through the paper machine in their present state—it is probable that the paper produced would be very uneven. Some spots in it would be very opaque and white, and others would be thin and translucent. The reason for this would be that the fibers had not interlocked sufficiently in spite of the sizing added to the pulp in the papermaking process. In order to be serviceable, paper must be entirely uniform, with no uneven spots where the fibers have not matted together. The paper that makes up this page has perfectly even distribution of fibers.

So the fibers themselves have to be treated in a special way known as *beating*. The pulp is carried from the storage tanks along water-filled troughs to the beating machine, which is an enormous cylindrically shaped

Bleached and washed pulp looks like popcorn when it reaches the beater

tank about four feet high and twenty feet in diameter. Into this the pulp is poured floating on quantities of water. At one end of this cylindrical tank is a huge iron wheel with many iron blades projecting from its rim. A cross section of it would look like a huge gearwheel. Sizing—starch, clay, and the like—is now added to the water in the beater, together with dye for coloring. The tinted bill forms and order pads we use are colored in this fashion. After thoroughly mixing these ingredients, the floating pulp, now sized and tinted (when necessary), is sent under this enormous scraping wheel which flattens the fibers and spreads them out so they will interlock with each other in the paper machine.

From the beaters the pulp is sent into the Jordan, a conical-shaped machine consisting of a shell and a plug revolving within that shell at a very high speed. Blunt bars protruding from the sides of the shell and the plug exert additional action, very much like the action in the beaters, as the pulp is forced by pump pressure through the machine. The Jordan is the final stage in the preparation of the fibers for papermaking. The processed fibers making up the pulp (which is now 99 per cent water) are now pumped into the head box located at the very beginning of the huge papermaking machine, called a *Fourdrinier,* that will turn the pulp into finished paper.

Sizing and dye for coloring is added to the water in the beater

Pulp gets its final refining treatment in Jordans like these

We have already mentioned the various processes that enter into the making of different kinds of paper. The two most important are: (1) the rate of flow of the saturated fibers over the screen; (2) the rate of speed of the machine itself. The rate of flow from the head box onto the screen and the rate of speed at which the machine shall run are carefully checked. If the flow is very rapid, the fibers will not have time to mat together closely and they will be loosely felted. If the machine rate is slow, the fibers will have more time to interlock, producing a thicker sheet that has body, strength, and opacity.

Also of great importance to the particular kind of paper to be produced is the amount and type of materials added to the pulp. These determine its sizing, as well as affect its density, brightness, smoothness, and other desirable qualities. The material that is mixed with the fibers in the beater and Jordan are usually clay, chalk, talc, zinc oxide, and titanium dioxide in varying proportions. All of these play a special part in producing fine paper—filling up the spaces among the fibers and turning out a strong, smooth writing surface or a tough sheet for packaging or other special uses.

By far the most interesting of all these added materials is titanium dioxide which was discovered only a few years ago. This powder or salt is whiter than the purest snow. No other powder or salt can match it for reflective brilliance. It is often used on advertising signs and outdoor billboards because the colors it produces are sometimes so brilliant that they appear to be lit up.

As the billions of tiny processed fibers, all suspended in the spongy mass, gush from the head box onto the moving screen and are carried along this screen, they are tossed and jostled together and over one another. The screen moves with two motions: a forward motion, which carries the fibers along, and a to-and-fro motion, which weaves and knits them together as the water drains off them.

At the other end of the wire screen is a large roller known as the *dandy-roll.* If the paper is to be watermarked (the best writing papers are watermarked, as you can see if you hold them to the light), it is done at this time. Special tooled-out metal designs press down on the wet sheet as it passes through the dandy-roll, squeezing out the fibers where it strikes and creating a watermark. By means of suction, the dandy-roll also transfers the wet sheet of woven fibers onto the first big felt roller in the machine.

From now on, the sole purpose of all the rollers that this sheet of water-soaked fibers will pass through is to dry them and smooth them out into an air-dried sheet of paper. The first rollers are covered with soft, specially prepared felt which helps dry the very wet sheet and

Pulp entering the head box

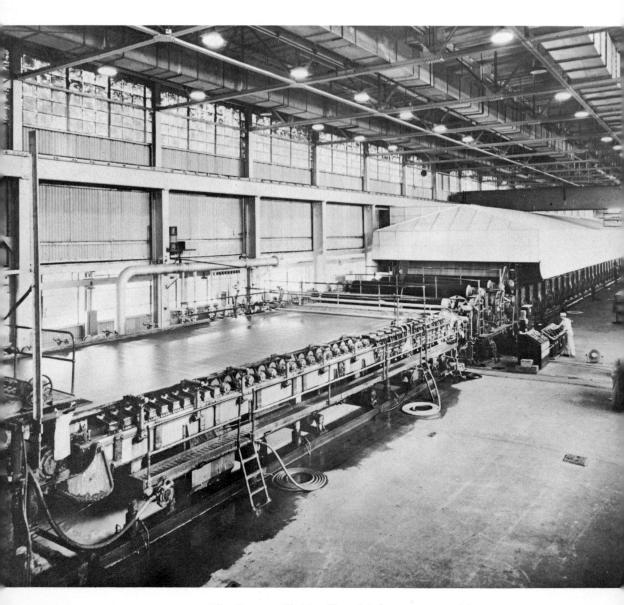

The "wet end" of a Fourdrinier paper machine

Water and pulp gush from the head box onto the moving screen

passes it on to the second roller which takes more of the moisture from it. As the sheet threads its way from one roller to another it is gradually dried. Then it enters the large heating rollers where it is threaded down from one to another for a distance of more than two hundred feet. And finally it emerges from the machine as a beautiful, continuous sheet of paper which is wound into a large roll at the far end of the machine.

The rate of speed at which the paper travels through the machine varies with the paper to be produced. Sometimes the speed is as much as twelve miles an hour, which means that in a fifteen-minute run, three miles of paper—sometimes twenty-two feet wide—is wound up, ready for shipment.

THE GROUNDWOOD, OR MECHANICAL, PROCESS

The groundwood, or mechanical, process of paper-making is extremely simple. As the name implies, this process consists of grinding wood on huge grindstones, and with the aid of great quantities of water, making it into a pulpy mass which closely resembles cooked oatmeal. Groundwood pulp is not treated chemically, and so it retains many of the resins and other impurities of

*The sheet of water-soaked fibers is dried by passing it through a
series of rollers*

Finished rolls of paper being lifted from the "dry end" of the machine

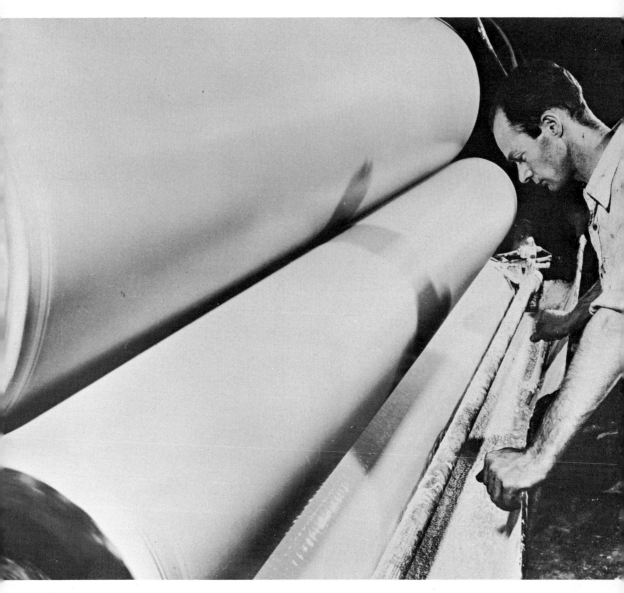

Some paper is given a finishing coat as it is rolled

Rolls of paper wrapped and stored for future shipment

the original wood. Consequently, paper made by this process is inferior in quality and lasting ability to book and writing papers. Eighty per cent of our newspapers are printed on groundwood paper called *newsprint.* It is ideal for that purpose, but after a year or so it turns brownish tan and will tear easily.

In this, as in the chemical process, bark is removed from the logs by tumbling them in a huge steel barrel about fifty feet long and ten to fifteen feet in diameter. After ten or fifteen minutes of this, they emerge completely debarked and are sent, by means of a conveyor, to the stone grinder. When the logs are pushed by hydraulic pressure against the huge stone wheels, which revolve at a speed of 150 revolutions per minute, the wood is turned into a powdery mass of loose fibers. Of course, the heat resulting from the friction between wood and stone is enormous and would not only set the wood on fire but would also burn the stone if it were not for the deluge of cold water that is constantly applied during the grinding. The flow of this water is carefully controlled to keep a constant temperature in the pulp of not more than 185°F. If the pulp is too hot or too cold, it will not mat properly in the paper machine; consequently, temperature is an extremely important consideration.

Today, sandstone wheels have been replaced by huge

Converters cut and trim the paper into sheets for special uses

Inspecting cut and finished sheets

synthetic stones. This is because the heating effects on sandstone ultimately damaged it and replacements were very costly. The synthetic stones have four to six times the life of the sandstone and produce more pulp in a given time. They are made of a substance called *carbo-rundum,* a compound of silicon and carbon, which is one of the hardest abrasive substances known. These stones are cut or burred into four different patterns depending upon the type of groundwood pulp to be produced. The fibers produced by synthetic stones are far better than those from the old sandstones, too, and consequently the quality of the paper is much better.

The ground-up wood pulp—about 98 per cent water to 2 per cent pulp—is sent straight into the head box of the papermaking machine, and from then on, the process of making it into paper is the same as that used for chemically processed papers.

Not all paper mills produce the pulp used in their plants. They buy it from plants that specialize in pulp. The pulp and paper industry is really divided into four main groups which, together, produce and control the distribution of paper everywhere.

These major specializations are as follows:

1. *Pulp-making.* These plants produce wood pulp either by chemical means or by wood-grinding. Many mills

produce only pulp and nothing else, selling it to paper mills.

2. *Pulp- and papermaking, as well as papermaking alone.* Some paper mills make pulp for their own use; others buy the pulp outside for use in their specialized machines. All paper that is produced from wood goes through the same general operation.

3. *Converters.* Regardless of where paper is produced, it is of no value in the mill. Its value lies in its conversion, and the manufacturers who do this are called *converters.* Either the paper is cut in sheets and sent to printers and publishers all over the country to be turned into books, magazines, advertising material, or other printed matter; or it is delivered to paperboard houses, which transform it by means of special machinery into board for boxes and cartons. Manufacturers of boxes, corrugated paper, cartons, and other paperboard products are converters. Other converters produce hundreds of different grades of paper for packaging and wrapping. Still other converters make photographic paper, blueprint paper, specialty paper for building construction, and other paper for special uses.

4. *Merchandising.* The paper merchant is the middleman of the paper industry. He buys great quantities of different kinds of paper from the mills or from the converters, and he stores them in his own plant until they are ordered by any one of the many different firms who

Hundreds of different grades of paper are used for packaging and wrapping

A high-speed box and carton label press

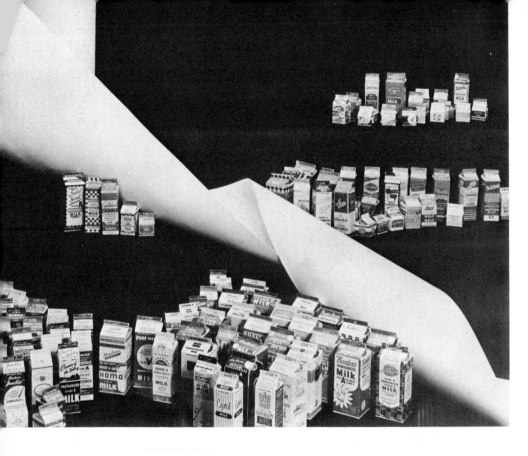

White converting boards and papers are used to meet the exacting specifications required for these end products

*More than 95 per cent of all merchandise sold today is wrapped in paper,
put up in paperboard boxes, or shipped in paper cartons*

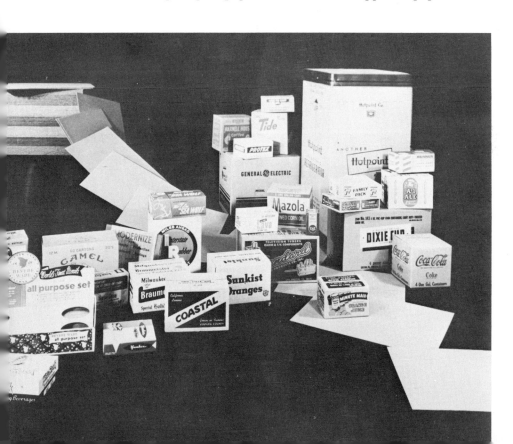

use paper. A printer, for example, may not order paper directly from the mill. He will order from one of the many paper houses, or distributors, located in large cities, and it's the paper house that buys from the mill. The same applies to stationers, food producers, candy companies, department stores, large shipping houses, and other business concerns.

PAPERBOARD

The value of paper for wrapping and shipping is just as great as its value in printing and publishing, photography, and advertising. More than 95 per cent of all merchandise sold today is either wrapped in paper, put up in paperboard boxes, both large and small, or shipped in cartons of every size and shape. The paperboard box and carton industries are enormous, rivaling the printing and publishing industries in their use of paper.

Although paper is thin, it can be made extremely tough, and with a little applied engineering, it is made into strong durable cartons. The engineering principle is that of the ancient Roman arch.

Consider a paper arch as shown in the diagram. Any weight put on the top of this will naturally push out the sides and flatten the arch.

But if the two ends of the arch are glued on a strip of paper, they cannot push out so easily and the weight is thus distributed along the strip. If another arch is added, upside down and touching this arch at its peak, and the ends of this arch are also glued to a strip of paper, the two arches will reinforce each other. A continuous series of these arches glued at the top and bottom by two strips of paper produces a light yet very tough and strong board known as *corrugated paperboard*. This paperboard is almost as strong and durable as wood, yet it is very much lighter, cheaper, and easier to produce. It is the material from which all cartons and cases used for shipping and transportation are made today.

How many millions of paperboard cartons are manufactured daily is anyone's guess. If you watch huge trucks load and unload merchandise in any large city, you will soon realize the vital importance of paper in shipping today. Almost everything is shipped in cartons. The pulp and paper industry supplies hundreds of thousands of tons of paper to converters who design cartons of every conceivable size and shape for every kind of product, ranging from large refrigerators, stoves, TV and radio sets, and washing machines to small items like toys, hardware, and machine parts. It is all paper and nothing more, and its strength and durability depend solely upon the ingenious construction of the paper corrugations and the top and bottom strips glued to them.

The process of producing corrugated paperboard from kraft paper—this simply means "strong paper"—is simple. The finished paper (most of it is unbleached) comes off the huge papermaking machines in enormous rolls. Because of the additives used in it and its particular method of production it is unusually strong and tough. The rolls are shipped to the converter who will turn them into cartons designed to meet the needs of the particular product it must carry.

Many things have to be considered by the carton designer: size, shape, and weight; how the carton is to be assembled and stored; how it is to be shipped; how it must be diecut and folded and printed so as to get the maximum strength and durability, and—at the same time—simplicity of unpacking. All these qualities must be carefully considered before a particular carton is made. Once they are determined, the rolls are put into the special machinery and the process of corrugating paperboard commences.

The paper is distributed through the machine on three

different rollers. The first corrugates the kraft paper by passing it between cylinders which are ribbed by many strips. A cross section of them resembles a gearwheel. As the paper passes between the cylinders it is instantly corrugated, or turned into continuous small paper arches upside down and right side up.

While this is proceeding, two flat papers—one at the top and the other at the bottom of the machine—are being unrolled into it and coated evenly with a thick glue. As the corrugated paper is led from the two rollers at the center, the glued papers from the top and bottom meet it and immediately fasten onto the top and bottom of the corrugated paper, forming the desired reinforcement.

The corrugated paperboard, smooth at top and bottom and stiff and strong, is now carried along the machine to where it is diecut, printed, and folded—all in one operation. When it leaves the machine it is thoroughly tested for resistance to bumping and compression. Then it is ready for shipment.

Paperboard for boxes and very small containers, sometimes called pasteboard, is usually made by gluing three or more sheets of paper together in the same type of machine used for making corrugated paperboard, except that the corrugating wheels are omitted. The paper is usually unbleached, but it is coated white on one side by applying a cream made from clay, satin white, titanium dioxide, and other pigments suspended in a solution of casein.

The white creamy paint is applied by three sets of brushes, their degree of stiffness varying as the paper moves forward. The first set of brushes are called *scrubbers,* because the brushes have stiff gray bristles which thoroughly clean the paper and make sure there are no tiny lumps on it. The second set of brushes are called *blenders;* these brushes spread the creamy paint on one side of the paper as it passes between a series of rolls and over a large cylinder on which it is held tight by rubber suction. The third set of brushes, made of soft badger hair, are *finishers,* which produce a fine, even, smooth white finish on the coated side of the paper.

Coated paperboard is then dried by hanging it up in large folds and circulating hot air through it. The white coating is now uniformly smooth, ink- and pigment-absorbing, and will not crack upon folding. When it is thoroughly dry, it is sent to a box manufacturer who diecuts, prints, and glues it to form the special type of box needed for a particular product.

Most boxes are produced in this way. Usually, the inside is not coated with paint and is therefore a grayish-brown color. Only the outside is coated so it can be imprinted. Boxes used for gloves, hosiery, shoes, and the

Corrugated shipping cartons are used to package and ship
goods of every description

like in department stores usually consist of raw paperboard covered with coated paper on which the name of
the store is printed. The main reason for coating only
one side of the paperboard is, of course, economy.

An attempt to describe the thousands of different
kinds of paper in use today and the various treatments
and properties used in them and on them would require
an encyclopedia.

We cannot conclude the story of paper without briefly
mentioning that most interesting and, at the same time,
most secret of all papers: currency.

The paper on which United States money is engraved
is produced especially for the Bureau of Engraving under
the most secret conditions by a private firm in New
England. Made strictly to Government specifications, it
contains cotton and linen with little threads of blue-and-
red fibers mixed with the pulp. It must stand a folding
test of 2,200 double folds without cracking or breaking
and has to undergo rigid tests of strength.

This distinctive paper is kept moist all the time. It is
moistened prior to delivery, and the packages contain a
uniform moisture content. It is kept at a required temperature in a damp vault at the Bureau of Engraving
until it is needed.

This special secret paper is one of the chief deterrents
to counterfeiting, for not one square inch of it is ever

allowed outside of the Bureau. Furthermore, no other manufacturer can make it, since it is a top secret of the Government. It is an interesting fact that the workers in the Bureau of Engraving are not searched when they leave at night. There is no need, for the amount of paper distributed in the morning when work begins is rigidly supervised. The paper is taken from the vault in large sheets and carefully computed as to weight and area, and every bit of the paper must be accounted for at the end of the day, including the thin slivers of waste material which remain after the currency is cut and trimmed.

We have mentioned many times the importance of paper to everyone, but here is a unique example of its importance. In no other firm or business house in the world is paper so carefully guarded as it is in the Bureau of Engraving in Washington, D.C.

INDEX

ABOUT THE AUTHOR

Jerome S. Meyer is the well-known author of many popular books for young people on scientific subjects. Born and educated in New York City, Mr. Meyer studied engineering at Columbia University, leaving to serve in the First World War. In 1925 he joined the staff of an advertising agency, two years later setting up his own agency. But his lifelong enthusiasm for science remained, and the result has been more than two dozen books on a variety of subjects.

Among his recent books are *The Book of Amazing Facts, Fun With Mathematics, World Book of Great Inventions, The Elements, Machines,* and *Prisms and Lenses.*